'Gripping…
hilarious.' *Guardian*

writing and
elegantly ghastly
pictures that
are a joy.'
Glasgow Herald

'Mortimer will
quickly be a real
favourite among
newly independent
readers.'
Birmingham Mail

'Fun, fast-paced
and engaging.'
South Wales Echo

'A wonderfully
inventive story,
superbly presented
and full of amazing
illustrations.'
Parents in Touch

'Humorous rhyming
text is well matched
amusing

First published in 2015 by Hodder Children's Books

Text copyright © Tim Healey 2015
Illustrations copyright © Chris Mould 2015

Hodder Children's Books, 338 Euston Road, London, NW1 3BH
Hodder Children's Books Australia, Level 17/207 Kent Street, Sydney, NSW 2000

A catalogue record of this book is available from the British Library.

ISBN 978 1 444 91970 7

Printed in China

MIX
From responsible
sources
FSC® C104740
FSC
www.fsc.org

Paper and board made from recycled material.

Hodder Children's Books is a division of Hachette Children's Books,
an Hachette UK Company

www.hachette.co.uk

MORTYMER Keene

ROBOT RIOT

Tim Healey and Chris Mould

Mortimer Keene

Age: 8
Special features: specs
Weak point: none!
Favourite phrase: 'I've just thought of something…'

Dario-B

Age: 1
Special features: designed to wait on staff
Weak point: spills a lot!
Favourite phrase: 'I am happy to serve you.'

4

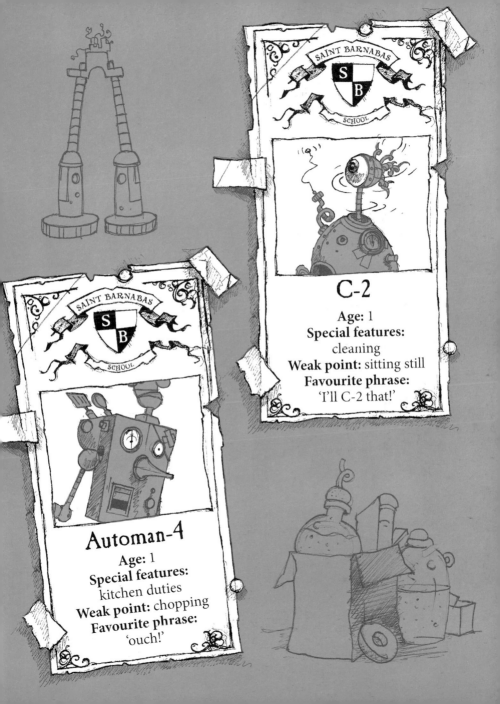

SAINT BARNABAS SCHOOL

S B

C-2

Age: 1
Special features:
cleaning
Weak point: sitting still
Favourite phrase:
'I'll C-2 that!'

SAINT BARNABAS SCHOOL

S B

Automan-4

Age: 1
Special features:
kitchen duties
Weak point: chopping
Favourite phrase:
'ouch!'

KT-Konception
Age: 1
Special features: designed for heavy lifting
Weak point: can only say 'bleep!'
Favourite phrase: 'bleep!'

E-Girl
Age: 1
Special features: electrics
Weak point: always wired
Favourite phrase: 'I'm shocked.'

L-Bo
Age: 1
Special features: designed for shoving
Weak point: a bit pushy
Favourite phrase:
'Shove off!'

Robo-13
Age: 1
Special features: suitable for all duties
Weak point: can get big-headed
Favourite phrase: 'My powers are limitless!'

Up in the science lab,
Mortimer Keene
Put a finishing touch
To his **Robo-13.**

Mr Green, the art teacher,
Looked in through the door.
'A robot! That's great!
Have you made any more?'

'Lots,' smiled the whizz kid,
'But I'm willing to bet
That **Robo-13**
Is the best I've made yet.'

Mr Green was impressed.
'He really looks ace.
I'm especially keen on
His nice, smiley face!'

The teacher then opened
A flap at the side,
And rummaged around
In the workings inside.

Mortimer warned,
'There's a **NEGATRON LOCK**.
Take care not to break it
Or give it a knock!'

But as Mr Green closed it,
Something slipped from a socket,
Spun through the air,
And dropped into his pocket!

'I'd better be off,'
Declared Mr Green.
'I'm expecting great things
From your **Robo-13!**'

Mortimer yawned:
'Now I'll get some sleep.'
And he dozed gently off…
While a sinister **BLEEP!**

Came from **Robo-13,**
Who started to stroll
To a laptop marked
MORTIMER'S ROBOT CONTROL…

The staff room at school
Had been quiet that day,
Till a neat little robot
Appeared with a tray.

'I'M happy to serve you
Your biscuits and tea,'
It bleeped very softly,
'I'M Dario-B.'

'Look, it's a robot!'
Exclaimed Mr Smart,
'That's pretty amazing –
A real work of art.'

Said Mrs Moray,
'I don't know about you,
But I think it's the doing
Of young You-Know-Who...'

Mortimer's robots –
The whizz kid's machines –
Were all around school
With some busy routines:

Down in the kitchen,
Automan-4
Was chopping up carrots
And onions galore.

E-Girl in reception
Was mending a fuse;

C-2 in the cloakroom

Was cleaning the loos…

Until **Robo-13**

Took that sinister stroll

To the laptop marked

Mortimer's Robot Control…

AND THEN ALL WENT
HAYWIRE!

Dario-B

Threw a plateful of biscuits
At Mrs MacNee.

Automan-4 grabbed
A strawberry mousse,
And poured the whole lot
Over Emily Bruce.

E-Girl in reception,
Waving a broom,
Chased Jeremy Harrison
All round the room.

C-2 in the cloakroom
Was tightening screws
To lock Anthony Lewis
In one of the loos!

'Find Mortimer Keene
Without further delay!
He MUST stop this nightmare!'
Cried Mrs Moray.

But up in the science lab,
Mortimer Keene…

…Had been tied to a chair
By his **Robo-13!**

'**Hah!**' bleeped the robot.
'**You poor little fool,
I am now in command
of St Barnabas School!**'

Through the lab doorway
Burst Mrs Moray,
With other staff members
In some disarray.

'STOP what you're doing,
At once! At the double!'
The head teacher fumed,
'Or you're in big trouble!'

'**BLEEP!**' went the robot.
'**D'you think I am mad?**
I'm not here to take orders.
I'm here to be BAD!

'**I am bent on DESTRUCTION!**
I'm here to do HARM!'

And he left with the laptop
Tucked under his arm.

Part Three

Mortimer Keene
Was scratching his head
As the teachers untied him.
'Wh-what's happening?' he said.

All through St Barnabas
Windows were smashed,
Teachers were terrorised,
Classrooms were trashed.

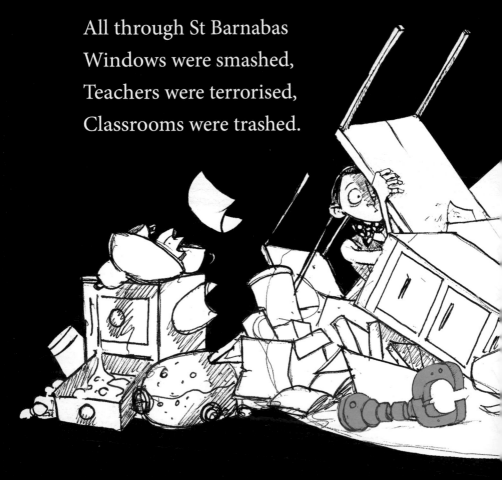

Reaching the staff room,
Robo-13

Gave a sinister chuckle
At what he had seen.

'**BLEEP!**' went the robot.
'Well done my crew!
Here's yet another
Instruction for you!

Go to reception
And block the front door.
We've done lots of damage
Now let's do some more!'

A lumbering robot
Called **KT-Konception**
Dragged a piano
Into reception.

'Grand!' chuckled L-BO,
'Just look what we've made,'
As he shunted it into
The big barricade.

52

The robot chief grinned:

'Let the real fun begin,
For none can get out,
And none can come in!'

Into the staff room
Mortimer flew,
With Mrs Moray
And Mr Green too.

Mr Field followed them
In through the door,

And wrestled the robot

Down onto the floor.

But **Dario B**

Came and grabbed hold

Of poor Mr Field

And knocked him out cold!

Robo-13

Quickly arose:

'I am harder to beat
Than you seem to suppose...'

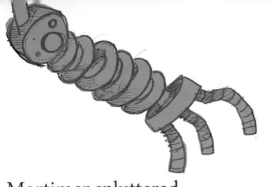

Mortimer spluttered,
'It's all such a shock!
Why are my robots
All running amok?'

'I have a confession,'
Declared Mr Green.
'It's something concerning
Your **Robo-13** . . .

'When I closed up the robot
I happened to knock it,
And this must have fallen out
Into my pocket!'

'The NEGATRON LOCK!'
Cried Mortimer Keene.
'I now see what's happened
To **Robo-13!**'

Mortimer pointed
A bleeper device
At the laptop control,

AND PRESSED
ON IT TWICE!

All of the robots
Stopped dead in their tracks.
'Phew,' breathed Mortimer,
'Now let's relax

For a minute or two.
And let's all take stock,
While I quickly replace
The Negatron Lock…'

'Now you have done that,'
Said Mrs Moray,
'You might pause to consider
What happened today.

You have caused the whole school
Unbelievable stress!
And who's going to tidy up
All of this mess?'

'We'll do it for you,'
Bleeped **Robo-13**.
'We will get everything
Tidy and clean.'

So the clear-up began.
And the robots took back
All the things they had piled
On the barricade stack.

They mended the windows
And swept all the floors,
And placed sticking-plasters
On bruises and sores.

Said Mrs Moray,
'It is all well and good,
But your robots are risky –
Is that understood?

It pains me to say it,
But as from today,
YOU ARE BANNED FROM THE LAB!'
Thundered Mrs Moray.

Mortimer Keene
Was sunk in despair.
After all he'd achieved
It seemed very unfair.

'I'm terribly sorry,'
Mr Green said,
'But think – you could always
Try painting, instead.'

'Yes!' cried Mortimer,
Grabbing a brush,
And setting to work
With his paints in a rush.

'Why are you smiling?'
Enquired Mr Green.
'I've just thought of something,'
Said Mortimer Keene…

Following these events, Mortimer's robots were sent for inspection to the Science Museum in London. Staff there spoke so highly of their construction that Mrs Moray relented and allowed Mortimer back in the lab.

Mortimer's
BARNABOTS

Mortimer Keene has drawn up
plans for robots designed to beat all
St Barnabas School records in sporting events.
Here are four of his prototypes:

Polo:
pole-vaulter

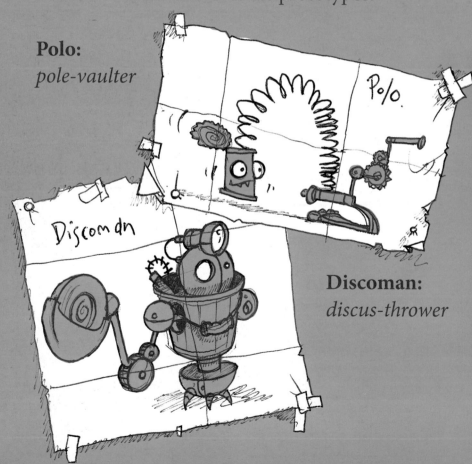

Polo.

Discoman

Discoman:
discus-thrower

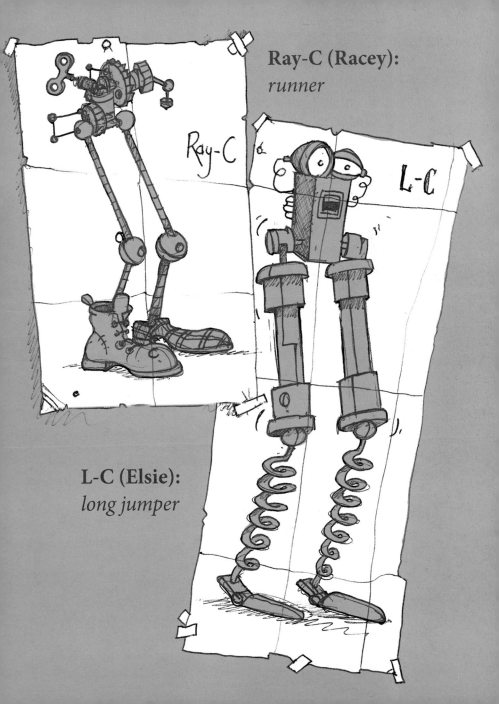

Ray-C (Racey):
runner

L-C

L-C (Elsie):
long jumper

Amazing Robot Facts

A robot dog called Genibo QD responds to over a hundred voice commands such as 'sit', 'come here!' and 'stand on your head'!

A robot rabbit (or rabbot) called Karotz has flapping ears, speaks four languages, and can tell you what the weather is like!

In 2013 a Japanese robot called Kirobo became the first talking humanoid in space. Kirobo is only 34 cm tall, and looks like a toy.

The first robot Olympics were held in 2013 in the United States, with 17 robots competing. Tasks ranged from climbing a ladder to steering a car.

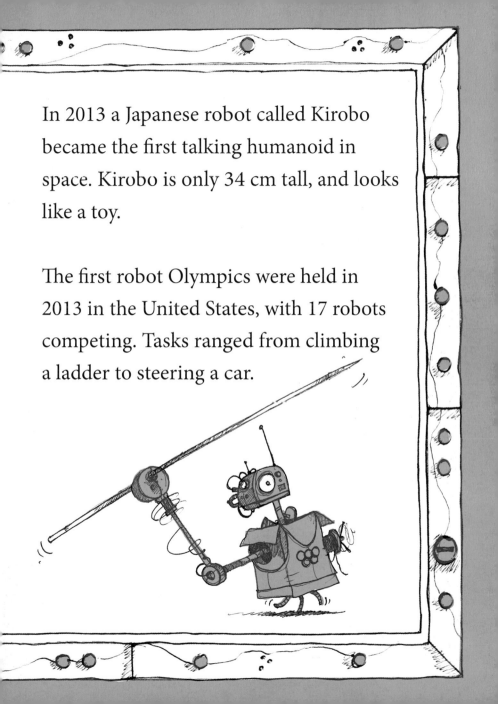

A-Z OF ROBOTS

Asimo - One of the most advanced robots in the world. He can dance to music, kick a football and climb stairs!

Bipedal robot - a two-legged robot.

Cyborg - a being which is partly robot and partly a living creature.

Deep Blue - first chess-playing computer to beat a human chess champion. Not strictly a robot, but it showed what robots might be capable of!

Elektro - famous humanoid robot first shown at the 1939 New York World's Fair.

Film robots - famous examples are C-3PO and R2-D2 who appear in Star Wars films.

Golem - a legendary humanoid, usually made of mud or stone. The name means 'shapeless mass'.

Humanoid - any being that looks human but isn't.

Intelligent machines - machines that can reason, learn and plan.

Japan - a top country for producing some of the most advanced and lifelike humanoids in the world.

Keepon - a small yellow robot designed in Japan to play with children and study their behaviour.

Lunokhod 1 - a Russian robot space vehicle. In 1970 it became the first unmanned rover to explore the Moon's surface.

Mini robot - any small robot. Many humanoid robots are made smaller than real people.

Nanorobot - a tiny robot with microscopic parts, built to work where humans can't go.

Octavia - a female humanoid robot invented in the USA to help fight fires.

Pleo - a robot pet dinosaur, designed in 2006. You can feed Pleo on rubber leaves. Cute!

Quickest robot – a four-legged American robot called Cheetah runs at 28.3 miles per hour!

Robot – any self-operating machine. Most are powered by electricity or electric batteries.

Scary! – common response to the latest robots.

Table tennis – a ping-pong-playing humanoid called Topio was developed in Vietnam.

Underwater robots – loads of robot machines have been created for walking or swimming under the sea.

Vacuum-cleaning robots – the first robot vacuum cleaner, called Roomba, came out in 2002.

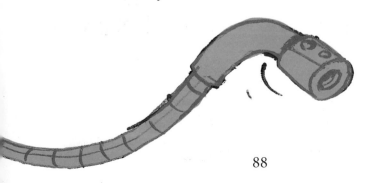

Why make robots? - they can run faster than us. They can beat us at chess. Be afraid, be very afraid…

Xylobots - robots that play xylophones.

Yellow robots - see Keepon (p85)

Zip it up - yup, running out of ideas for the alphabet. Let's zip it up now…

Robot Quiz

How much do you know about robots? This quiz is designed to test your knowledge. (Answers can all be found in the A-Z of Robots.)

1. R2-D2 and C-3PO are robots in a famous film called:

a) Robot Wars

b) Star Wars

c) Calamity Jane

2. A Roomba is:

a) a ballroom dance for robots

b) the sound of a robot burping

c) a vacuum-cleaning robot

3. Nanorobots are:
a) robot nannies

b) tiny robots with microscopic parts

c) banana-shaped robots

4. A bipedal robot has:
a) two legs

b) four legs

c) a bicycle

5. A keepon is:
a) a keeper of robots

b) a small yellow robot

c) a warm, woolly jumper

Robot Racer

Most modern robots are electronic. But people have also made robots powered by clockwork, fluids and air pressure, amongst other things. Here's how to make a robot racer using a rubber band.

You will need

- Cotton reel
- Rubber band (you will probably need a couple of spares!)
- Matchstick
- Strong tape
- Washer
- Pencil or stick

What you do

1. Put a rubber band through the hole in the middle of a cotton reel.

2. Loop one end around a matchstick and tape it down.

3. At the other end of the cotton reel, thread the rubber band through a washer and pull it tight.

4. Put a pencil through the loop of the rubber band, poking out through the washer.

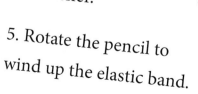

5. Rotate the pencil to wind up the elastic band.

6. Put your racer on the floor and watch it go!

MORTIMER KEENE

ALIEN
ABDUCTION

Tim Healey and
Chris Mould

978 0 340 99775 8

MORTIMER KEENE

DINO
DANGER

Tim Healey and
Chris Mould

978 1 444 91969 1

KEENE

ROBOT
RIOT

Tim Healey and
Chris Mould

978 1 444 919707

BEWARE!

Mortimer's madcap plans and crazy ideas could rub off on you!